ANTONÍN DVOŘÁK

CARNIVAL

Overture for Orchestra
Op. 92

T0081275

Ernst Eulenburg Ltd

London · Mainz · Madrid · New York · Paris · Prague · Tokyo · Toronto · Zürich

PREFACE/VORWORT

On August 1, 1891, Dvořák wrote to a friend that he had 'finished the new overture which I had begun in Prague. How it will be named, I don't know yet – but in the papers I have read that it will be called „Summer night". These people hear something somewhere and then set traps for me – yet they know nothing.'[1] All the same, the journalists were not completely misinformed; the first sketch of the overture in question bears three different titles, 'Lyric overture', 'Amid Nature' and 'Summer Night', and a further subtitle, 'In Solitude'.[2] The whole overture was sketched between March 31 and April 18, and finished in score on July 8, 1891. On July 28 Dvořák began the sketches for a second overture which he called 'Life', with the subtitle 'Carnival'; the sketch was finished on August 14, the score on September 12. A third overture was begun in November and the last page of the sketch is dated – with Dvořák's customary thanks to God – January 14, 1892; the score had already been begun on December 10 and was finished on January 18; this third overture was entitled 'Love' and 'Othello'. On April 28, on the eve of his departure for America, Dvořák conducted the first performance of all three, by the augmented orchestra of the National Theatre, in the Rudolfinum at Prague; they were described on the programme on that occasion as 'Nature', 'Life (Czech carnival)' and 'Love (Othello)' and bore the collect-

Am 1. August 1891 schrieb Dvořák an einen Freund: „Ich habe die neue Ouvertüre beendet, die ich in Prag angefangen habe. Wie ich sie nennen werde, weiss ich noch nicht – aber in den Zeitungen habe ich gelesen, dass sie 'Sommernacht' heissen soll. Diese Leute hören oft etwas läuten und suchen mich zu fangen – aber sie wissen gar nichts."[1] Gleichwohl waren die Journalisten nicht ganz schlecht unterrichtet; die erste Skizze der Ouvertüre trägt drei verschiedene Titel: „Lyrische Ouvertüre", „In der Natur" und „Sommernacht" und einen weiteren Untertitel: „In Einsamkeit".[2] Die ganze Ouvertüre wurde zwischen dem 31. März und 18. April skizziert und am 8. Juli in der Partitur beendet. Am 28. Juli begann Dvořák die Skizzen für eine zweite Ouvertüre, die er „Leben" nannte, mit dem Untertitel „Karneval"; die Skizze wurde am 14. August beendet, die Partitur am 12. September. Eine dritte Ouvertüre wurde im November begonnen, und die letzte Seite der Skizze hat das Datum 14. Januar 1892, mit Dvořáks üblichem Dank an Gott; die Partitur war schon am 10. Dezember begonnen worden und wurde am 18. Januar beendet; diese dritte Ouvertüre wurde „Liebe" und „Othello" benannt. Am 28. April, dem Vorabend seiner Abreise nach Amerika, dirigierte er selbst die Erstaufführung aller drei, mit dem verstärkten Orchester des National-Theaters im Rudolfinum in Prag; auf dem betreffenden Programm waren sie bezeichnet als: „Na-

[1] *Antonin Dvořák Přátelùm Doma*, ed. Otakar Šourek (Prag, 1941)
[2] Otakar Šourek, *Dvořákovy Skladby Orchestrálni*, Vol. II (Prag, 1946)

[1] *Antonin Dvořák Prátelùm Doma*, hrsg. v. Otakar Šourek, Prag 1941
[2] Otakar Šourek, *Dvořákovy Skladby Orchestrálni*, Bd. II, Prag 1946

ive opus-number 91. Even before the third was finished, Dvořák had told his publisher Simrock that 'the three overtures form a cycle and the title „Nature, Life and Love" (naturally for orchestra), have a common opus-number, and can also be played each be itself'.[3] But for some time he then seems to have cooled to the titles altogether; he speaks in his letter only of the 'three overtures' and if he wishes to distinguish them he does so only by key. Even as late as November 1893 he was still undecided. 'The overtures originally had a title, „Nature, Life and Love"', he wrote to Simrock. 'However as each overture forms a self-contained whole, I should like to alter the title, on theses lines:
Overture in F major („Amid Natur"), Op. 91
Overture in A major („Carnival"), Op. 92
Overture in F sharp minor „Othello" or „tragic" or „Eroica"? Op. 93

Perhaps you can think of something better? Or shall we leave it simply „Overture"? But it's to some extent *programme-music* all the same'.
The overtures were ultimately issued by Simrock in March 1894, in score, parts and four-hand piano arrangements by Suk and Nedbal, as 'Amid Nature', 'Carnival' and 'Othello', with separate opus-numbers (91, 92, 93). The first proofs of the overtures and the 'Dumky' Trio were actually corrected by Brahms, as the composer himself was in America: a kindness which touched Dvořák deeply. According to Šourek, the autograph scores of 'Amid Nature' and 'Carnival' bear dedications respectively to the University of Cam-

tur", „Leben (Tschechischer Karneval)" und „Liebe (Othello)" und trugen die gemeinsame Opuszahl 91. Schon ehe die dritte vollendet war, teilte Dvořák seinem Verleger Simrock mit: „Diese drei Ouvertüren bilden einen Cyclus und haben den Titel: Natur, Leben und Liebe (natürlich für Orchester), haben eine gemeinsame Opuszahl und kann auch jede für sich gespielt werden."[3] Aber eine Zeitlang schien er an den Titeln nicht mehr interessiert; er spricht in seinen Briefen nur von den „drei Ouvertüren", und als Unterscheidung nennt er lediglich die Tonart. Noch im November 1893 war er unentschlossen; er schrieb an Simrock: „Die Ouvertüren hatten ursprünglich den Titel: 'Natur, Leben und Liebe'. Weil aber jede Ouvertüre ein ganzes für sich bildet, will ich den Titel ändern, und zwar so:
Ouvertüre F-dur ('In der Natur'), Op. 91
Ouvertüre A-dur ('Karneval'), Op. 92
Ouvertüre Fis-moll ('Othello' oder 'tragische' oder 'Eroica'?), Op. 93
Wüssten Sie vielleicht etwas Besseres? Oder soll man einfach 'Ouvertüre' lesen? Aber *Programm-Musik* ein wenig ist es doch!"
Die Ouvertüren wurden schließlich im März 1894 von Simrock herausgegeben, und zwar in Partitur und Stimmen sowie Klavierauszug von Suk und Nedbal, unter den Titeln: „In der Natur", „Karneval" und „Othello", mit getrennten Opuszahlen 91, 92, 93. Die ersten Korrekturen der Ouvertüren und des „Dumky"-Trios wurden während Dvořák selbst in Amerika war, von Brahms gelesen; eine Gefälligkeit, die Dvořák tief berührte. Nach Šourek trugen die Autographen von „In der Natur" und „Karneval" Widmungen

[3] *Simrock-Jahrbuch* II, Berlin 1929

bridge and the Czech University of Prague, both of which had recently conferred honorary doctorates on the composer: neither dedication appears in the published scores.

Šourek tell us that 'so far as it is possible to judge from some remarks scribbled in the scores and partly according to statements inspired by him which have been put on record, Dvořák wished in this cycle to draw in overture-form musical pictures of three of the most powerful impressions of the solitary, wrapped about by the exalted stillness of the summer night, the impression of a man seized into the joyous vortex of life, and finally the feeling of a man in the power of a violent love poisoned by jealousy. In more concise terms: to present nature itself, free acceptance of it, and distortion of it'. The motto-theme common to all three overtures is therefore not simply a musical device for connecting the three parts of the triptych; it is the theme of 'nature', naturally predominant in the first piece, appearing only distantly or episodically in 'Carnival' (but not merely in the clarinet solo of the *Andantino con moto*, p. 28, as is sometimes thought; the opening theme, bars 3-6, is clearly derived from it), clouded over or distorted harmonically and orchestrally in 'Othello'.

Gerald Abraham

an die Universität Cambridge bzw. die tschechische Universität Prag, die beide kurz zuvor Dvořák das Ehren-Doktorat verliehen hatten; doch erscheint keine der Widmungen auf den Druckausgaben.

Šourek erzählt uns: „Aus flüchtigen Bemerkungen in den Partituren und aus Erklärungen, die von ihm stammen und aufgezeichnet wurden, geht hervor, dass Dvořák in diesem Zyklus ein musikalisches Bild der mächtigen Einwirkungen auf das menschliche Gemüt in Ouvertürenform entwerfen wollte: den Eindruck der Einsamkeit, umhüllt von der erhabenen Stille der Sommernacht, den Eindruck eines Menschen, der in den heiteren Strudel des Lebens gerissen wird, und endlich das Gefühl eines Menschen, der von einer heftigen Liebe, vergiftet durch Eifersucht, beherrscht wird. In kürzeren Worten: die Natur selbst, ihr freier Spielraum und ihre Entstellung." Das allen drei Stücken gemeinsame Motto ist daher nicht einfach ein musikalischer Plan, die drei Teile eines Triptychons zu verbinden; es ist das Thema „Natur", das natürlich in dem ersten Stück vorherrscht, während es in „Karneval" nur entfernt und episodisch erscheint (aber nicht ausschließlich in dem Klarinetten-Solo des *Andantino con moto*, S. 28, wie zuweilen angenommen wird; das Eröffnungsthema, T. 3-6, ist klar davon abgeleitet); in „Othello" ist es verschleiert und durch Harmonie und Instrumentation verzerrt.

Gerald Abraham

CARNIVAL
Overture

Ant. Dvořák, Op. 92
1841—1904

K

00000000000000000000000000000000

58

R

410

R

66

460

510

E. E. 6013